Number Resources YEAR 1

For Numeracy Lessons

by Annie Owen

Contents

Introduction

The elements of numeracy – whether knowledge, understanding or skills – follow a loose hierarchy. The structure is sometimes obvious, as in the ability to bridge through ten before learning to bridge through twenty. However, in other areas the sequence can be blurred. Which comes first, knowing that addition can be done in any order or knowing that more than two numbers can be added together? Knowing addition facts to ten, or the corresponding subtraction facts?

Children can learn such concepts at different times and in different orders. All teachers know that it is nigh impossible to predict how much will be absorbed by any individual child at first meeting and that concepts need to be revisited after a suitable gap. Because children themselves choose what is absorbed and what is rejected, any collection of children is naturally a mixed ability group.

Given these two factors – the need to revisit concepts and the need to cater for a wide range of ability – schools need resources for numeracy which are flexible and easily adaptable. This book is an attempt to provide just that.

Many of the resources are easily changed to provide experience at different levels. There is also a good deal of cross-referencing, several resources being of use for a particular concept.

The teacher's notes are organised around statements from the National Numeracy Framework (NNF). They are not comprehensive, being a support resource, but may provide teachers with ideas for areas of the number curriculum not covered here. The division of the ideas into books for separate years is for ease of access, but the resources can be used across all ages as ability requires. The additional resource book, *Teacher's Templates for Numeracy KS1*, gives further flexibility for revisiting concepts at different levels of difficulty and hence also supports mixed ability teaching.

Some schools may wish to consider using the worksheets for homework, obviously taking into account that parents would need access to the appropriate teacher's notes.

Vocabulary

All vocabulary used on the worksheets is consistent with the recommendations of the NNF Mathematical Vocabulary Book.

A note about order

For ease of use, the concepts are met here in the order of the NNF's Teaching Programme. This is not necessarily the order in which they are taught, this being loosely defined by the Framework but finally decided by each school.

A note about problem-solving

Wherever possible, the activities have been opened up to allow children exploration. Theoretically, therefore, very many activities can be mapped to :

NNF:62   Solve simple mathematical problems or puzzles; recognise and predict from simple patterns and relationships. Suggest extensions by asking 'What if ...?' or 'What could I try next?'

However, this would be repetitious and this mapping is hence only made where it is the main objective of the activity (eg Worksheets 25 and 26).

Teacher's notes

NNF: National Numeracy Framework

TTN KS1: Teacher's Templates for Numeracy KS1 *(published by Evans)*

A note about recitation

Counting to twenty, counting in tens, twos or in fives are essentially oral activities. Hence, worksheets are not appropriate, though counting along a number line (Worksheet 1) provides a bridge between recitation and counting objects. Worksheet 7 (Fingers and toes) can be used to introduce the idea of counting in fives, before the children begin to learn the number string. Also, the number cards in TTN KS1 can be used to provide starting and stopping numbers. The 100 square (TTN KS1) can be used as an aid to counting on or back in tens from any number to 100.

NNF mappings in bold type are Key Objectives for this year group.

1 Dotty numbers

NNF:	2	Know the number names and recite them in order to at least 20
	8	**Read ... numerals from 0 to at least 20**

The use of this worksheet is quite obvious. Use as reinforcement as soon as the children can read the numerals, or as assessment at the end of a teaching programme on the 1–20 numerals. You may wish to cover the numerals with written words. This would provide some differentiation. Also try completing the picture backwards from 20.

2 Party pieces

and

3 More party pieces

NNF:	2	**Count reliably at least 20 objects**
	8	**Read and write numerals from 0 to at least 20**

With young children, the use of real objects is preferable to 2-D pictures for counting. Children can then move the objects as they count (and hence keep a check on which objects have already been counted), or can arrange them in a way which makes them more easy to count. These two worksheets are therefore suitable for children who no longer need these aids to their counting. They also provide a record of progress. A follow-up activity could be to make a class poster from some other walk of life (eg. school play, or the seaside) where the children choose the objects for each number.

4 Chocolate bars

NNF:	2	**Count reliably at least 20 objects.**
	8	Begin to know what each digit in a two-digit number represents, partition a 'teens' number
	14	**Order numbers to at least 20**

This worksheet provides more counting to 20, but with the emphasis on partitioning the numbers into 'tens' and 'ones', i.e. it emphasises the worth of the tens digit. Children should count the pieces of chocolate and write down the number. The sheet can then be cut up and the numbers placed in order, perhaps sticking them on to a strip of paper to make a frieze. They can also be used as number cards for other counting activities (e.g. with two sets, play snap or Pelmanism).

Once the children have some experience of counting to 20, encourage them to 'count on' from ten.

5 House numbers

NNF:	2,4,6	Count on in twos from zero, then one, and begin to recognise odd or even numbers to about 20 as 'every other number'

House numbers are an obvious and everyday example of odds and evens. Point these out to the children on any trip walking outside school. This worksheet should be followed up with chanting of the evens or odds at mental maths times. Point out, or ask a child to point out, the numbers on a number line while chanting. Can they continue past 20? Would 24 be odd or even? What about 27? If the children are ready, you may wish to discuss the fact that ALL odds end in either 1,3,... and all the evens in 2, 4, ...

6 Odds and evens

NNF: 2,4,6 Begin to recognise odd or even numbers to about 20 as 'every other number'

Use this worksheet as a follow-on from number 5. Ask the children to complete the hops on the evens number line and to colour the numbers they get in red on the two squares.

Repeat for the odd numbers, using a different colour. In a plenary, discuss the patterns the odds and evens make. Can anyone explain why the two tables give different patterns? You may wish to also look at a 100 square, or limit this to the top two lines. All these activities underline the relationship between odds and evens (i.e. their alternate nature). The worksheet can be extended by hopping on the 100 snake (TTN KS1).

7 Fingers and toes

NNF: 2,4,6 … count in steps of 5 from zero to 20

As with all counting, counting in fives is primarily an oral activity. However, it is useful to have the children find the numbers themselves, before learning to chant them. The worksheet can also be used as an assessment item. Can the children carry on the pattern on blank paper (or on the 100 snake – TTN KS1)?

8 Number snakes

NNF: 2,4,6 Describe and extend number sequences
62 Recognise and predict from simple patterns and relationships

This worksheet covers all the counting sequences expected at Year 1: counting in 2s, 5s, 10s, counting forwards and backwards and also the 'begin to' skill of counting in 3s. It would therefore make a good assessment item for the end of the year. To practise any particular sequence, use the blank snakes (TTN KS1), writing in parts of some sequences and leaving the children to make up some of their own. They can also make up sheets for a friend (in itself a useful diagnostic tool!).

9 Multibase numbers

and

10 Abacus numbers

NNF: 8 Begin to know what each digit in a two-digit number represents

This first experience of place value is extremely important, being the chief building block of our number system. After counting, and after bundling their counted objects into tens and units, the next step is to represent the tens by some object/symbol which is not obviously made of ten separate items. Multibase is a traditional bridge between these two concepts, as the ten units can still be seen on the tens (or 'longs'), yet it is one object which is handled to represent each ten.

A possible next step is to replace tens with single counters, but of a different colour from the units. For all these (from bags of pine cones to coloured counters), impress upon the children that it is important where we place the objects. Tens must go on the left, units on the right.

Finally, children progress to the knowledge that it is only the position of the counters which determines their worth. The abacus worksheet fulfils this role, with all counters looking the same. (If you do not have any abaci, use set circles to hold counters, arranged side by side.)

With both worksheets, let children make up their own examples, or make up questions for others (see TTN KS1).

11 Flags

NNF: 10 **Understand and use the vocabulary of comparing and ordering numbers**
Compare two familiar numbers, say which is more or less, and give a number which lies between them

You will need cut-out copies of the flags from Worksheet 13. The units should be turned over and jumbled, so that the children choose them randomly.

The children choose two units and use them to make two 'teens' numbers. They must then choose which number will go where in the first question and write down a number which is in between them. They can use the Ski race number line (see Worksheet 13) to help them if necessary. At the bottom of the page, children choose which words to use.

This worksheet continues the progression in place value concepts, numerals only being used, and the worth of the tens being reinforced by their position on the flags and their role in the activity.

12 More or less

NNF: 12   **Within the range 0 to 30, say the number that is 1 or 10 more or less than any given number**

The children will need number cards, more-less dice and a blank dice labelled 1, 1, 1, 10, 10, 10, (all found in TTN KS1). You can change the level of this activity by the cards used. Let the children use a number line, or 100-snake if necessary.

13 Ski race

NNF: 8   Partition a 'teens' number
14   **Order a set of numbers to 20** and position them on a number track

This resource looks at tens and units more abstractly. The children should cut out the flags, jumble them up and then fit tens and units flags together to make 'teens' flags. These can then be placed in order and recorded, along with numbers to 10, on the ski race picture. Make an extra copy of the units flags to enable the children to have all the 'real' flags together, if they would benefit.

14 Number sentences

NNF: 10   **Understand and use the vocabulary of comparing and ordering numbers**
24, 28   Understand the operation of addition, and of subtraction … and use the related vocabulary

Each pair of children needs one set of number trios (eg. 10, 3, 7) and all the rest of the sheet. They should cut out all the words and use them to make as many different sentences about their trio as they can, perhaps recording these on paper. If you photocopy this on to acetate, the children can make their sentences on an OHP. Alternatively, enlarge on to card, and attach the pieces to a 'washing line' with pegs to make sentences.

15 Domino sums

NNF: 24, 28   Begin to recognise that addition can be done in any order

Use real dominoes, if possible, to demonstrate how the sum changes when the domino is turned around. What do the children notice about their answers? At the plenary, show them a domino one way, and discuss the sum. Can they tell you the other sum without turning the domino around? Continue this activity on blank paper, using domino numbers (Number Resources Year R Worksheet 2) or real dominoes.

16 Connect 3

NNF: 26   Begin to recognise that more than two numbers can be added together

Each child to choose a different colour pen. Children take it in turns to roll a dice and put a ring round one example of the number they get. The aim is to get three numbers in a line which add up to 10 (diagonals count too) in their colour. You can continue the play, counting up how many lines each child has at the end.

17 The story of ___

NNF: 24, 28   Begin to recognise that addition can be done in any order
30   Begin to know addition facts for all pairs of numbers with a total up to at least 10

Either give children numbers or let them generate them randomly using number cards 5–10 (TTN KS1). The children should partition their number in as many ways as they can find, drawing two pictures and writing two numerals to show the partition. They can use counters to help. You may wish to have the class concentrate on facts to 10, as this is one set of facts they need to learn by heart at this stage. At the plenary, emphasise by questioning that, for example 3 + 7 gives the same as 7 + 3. Can they find other examples which 'switch round'? Also, this is a good opportunity to pick out doubles and use the language of doubling and halving. Which numbers don't have any halves?

18 What's left?

NNF: 30   Begin to know … and the corresponding subtraction facts
34   Use patterns of similar calculations

This worksheet introduces the symbolic representation of subtraction and reinforces the number facts to 10. Use counters to cover up the images. Children can randomly generate numbers for the bottom half of the sheet using dice or number cards, and continue using any of the pictures to find other facts, which they record on the back or on plain paper. At the plenary, or as a group, record the facts in order (10–1, 10–2 etc.) and ask the children what they notice.

19 Grouping 5s

NNF: 32   Begin to partition into '5' and a bit when adding 6, 7, 8 or 9 then recombine

This is a difficult concept, as there is little structured apparatus to help children with partitioning into '5 and a bit'. The worksheet from the Reception Book – Flashy Buttons, Page 3 – shows the numbers 6–10 as buttons arranged with 5 of them in a 'five holder'. You could use this sheet, or make 'five holders', to demonstrate what is happening here. It is unlikely that the children will be able to do this worksheet without some preliminary input. Use number cards 5–10 to generate the numbers.

20 Next-door numbers

NNF: 32   Identify near doubles, using doubles already known (e.g. 6 + 5)

Each pair of children needs two sets of number cards 1–10 (TTN KS1). One set is jumbled and placed face down. The other set is spread out to be easily seen. One child turns over a hidden card and writes the number in the first box. The second child chooses a 'next-door' number (one more or one less) and writes that in the second box. The children then work out the answer together, taking turns to write it in. Encourage the children to talk about the number which is doubled.

21 Add 9 machines

NNF: 34   Add 9 to single-digit numbers by adding 10 then subtracting 1

Before distributing the worksheet, revise with the children what happens when we add ten to single-digit numbers. Use the worksheet picture or some model of a machine (a soap carton makes a good model) to feed numbers in and out. What would happen if we made the machine be a 'Take away 1' machine? Explain to the children that they are going to use an 'Add 9' machine. The numbers they feed in will be found using a spinner or a 1–9 dice. They can use counters or a number line to help.

At the plenary, ask if anyone noticed anything interesting about their answers. Can anyone explain (perhaps on the number line) why this happens?

22 Grouping 10s

NNF: 36, 38   Use known number facts and place value to add or subtract a pair of numbers mentally within the range 0 to at least 10, then 0 to at least 20

This concept is one of the hardest for this year group and comes towards the end of the year. Use number cards 10–14 to generate the numbers. If you want to introduce larger numbers than 14, they must be paired with another two-digit number so that the total does not exceed 19, and you will hence need to provide the numbers yourself. The number line work could be supported by, or replaced by, Multibase equipment.

23 Needs and leaves

NNF: 40   Begin to bridge through 10, and later 20, when adding a single-digit number

This worksheet deals with the second half of the statement. Show the children on a number line that the aim is to make 20 and then count on from there. How many do we NEED to make 20? What will that LEAVE from the number we were asked to add? The second half of the page is for you to provide examples, or ask the children to make up some. Recording a bridging in this form is theoretically not required until Year 3, though many Key Stage 1 children are able to use it. If your children are not ready, then leave the activity as an oral one only.

24 Think of a number

NNF: 60   Choose and use appropriate number operations and mental strategies to solve problems

Once children get the idea of this activity, it provides an excellent '5 minute' filler. Begin by setting the question yourself, for the class to work out. Can the children tell you how they got the answer? They can then play amongst themselves, but to avoid cheating, insist that the question poser has to write the answer down on a piece of paper before asking the question!

The worksheet provides a record of the children's progress in this area.

25 Tree puzzle

NNF: 62   Solve simple mathematical problems or puzzles

This puzzle can be extended by using two cards of any three consecutive numbers (eg: 5, 5, 6, 6, 7, 7). If children find it difficult, suggest they replace the cards with counters of the same worth.

26 Darts

NNF: 62   Solve simple mathematical problems or puzzles
                    Suggest extensions by asking 'What if…?' or 'What could I try next?'

Other teaching points:

NNF: 24, 28   Begin to recognise that addition can be done in any order.
       26   Begin to recognise that more than two numbers can be added together.

Give children a number between 12 and 20, let them choose their own, or use number cards (TTN KS1) to generate the numbers randomly. Numbers can be 'hit' more than once but all three darts must be used.

During the activity, encourage children to put the larger numbers first. Look for other strategies the children use and encourage them, for example, using near-doubles or partitioning into '5 and a bit'. Discuss any such strategies used by the children in the plenary.

Discuss with the children, or with individuals, that, when we have one solution, what could we do to the numbers to make another set. For example, if the total is 15 and they suggest 8 + 3 + 4, we could take one from the 3 and add it to the 8 to make 9 + 2 + 4.

27 Tell me a story

NNF: 66, 68, 70   **Use mental strategies to solve simple problems** set in 'real life'

It is important that the children realise that there is more than one number sentence to describe the pictures (eg 6 = 3 + 3) and hence many different stories. Find as many different ones as possible for the plenary. The three lines at the bottom are for children to describe the second story. They can also make up their own.

28 Ways to pay

NNF: 68   Recognise coins of different values. Work out how to pay an exact sum using smaller coins

This worksheet can easily be adapted for differing abilities by providing different coins or different numbers of coins and changing the prices.

29 Change game

NNF: 68   Find totals and change from up to 20p

The children throw a normal dice in turn, collecting equivalent money and exchanging coins whenever necessary. They cannot pay for an item with the exact money, but must use the next coin(s) up. For example, if they want to buy something for 16p they must pay with a 20p. A 12p item could be paid for with a 10p and a 5p. The children must say how much change they will get and then collect their change, which is placed in a separate pile and the child begins again with a clean slate. The first child to have more than 20p in the 'change' pile is the winner.

30 School fair

NNF: 68   Recognise coins of different values. Work out how to pay an exact sum using smaller coins

On this final sheet, children need to connect with a drawn line each stall price to a purse. Alternatively, the money can be 'whited out' and the children draw (or write) the money they need, having collected it first from a pool of plastic or paper money. Another alternative is to give the children 20p, 25p or 30p and ask them to work out and draw (or write) the change they will get.

Mapping to the National Numeracy Framework – Year 1

● main objectives ○ other objectives	1	2	3	4	5	6	7	8
2	Know the number names and recite them in order to at least 20	●							
2	Count reliably at least 20 objects		●	●	●				
2,4,6	Count on in twos from zero, then one, and begin to recognise odd or even numbers to about 20 as 'every other number'					●	●		●
2,4,6	… count in steps of 5 from zero to 20							●	●
2,4,6	Describe and extend number sequences								●
8	Read… numerals from 0 to at least 20	●	●	●					
8	…write numerals from 0 to at least 20		●	●					
8	Begin to know what each digit in a two-digit number represents, partition a 'teens' number				●				
10	Understand and use the vocabulary of comparing and ordering numbers								
10	Compare two familiar numbers, say which is more or less, and give a number which lies between them								
12	Within the range 0 to 30, say the number that is 1 or 10 more or less than any given number								
14	Order numbers to at least 20				●				
24, 28	Understand the operation of addition, and of subtraction … and use the related vocabulary								
26	Begin to recognise that more than two numbers can be added together								
30	Begin to know addition facts for all pairs of numbers with a total up to at least 10								
32	Begin to partition into '5' and a bit when adding 6, 7, 8 or 9 then recombine								
32	Identify near doubles, using doubles already known (e.g. 6 + 5)								
34	Add 9 to single-digit numbers by adding 10 then subtracting 1								
36, 38	Use known number facts and place value to add or subtract a pair of numbers mentally within the range 0 to at least 10, then 0 to at least 20								
40	Begin to bridge through 10, and later 20, when adding a single digit number								
60	Choose and use appropriate number operations and mental strategies to solve problems								
62	Solve simple mathematical problems or puzzles								
66, 68, 70	Use mental strategies to solve simple problems set in 'real life'								
68	Recognise coins of different values								
68	Find totals and change from up to 20p								
68	Work out how to pay an exact sum using smaller coins								

9	10	11	12	13	14	15	16	17	18	19	20	21	22	23	24	25	26	27	28	29	30
●	●	●																			
●	●	●		●																	
		●			●																
		●																			
			●																		
				●																	
					●	●		●							●		○	○		○	
							●										○		○		○
								●	●												
										●											
											●										
												●									
													●								
														●							
															●						
																●	●				
																		●			
																			●		●
																				●	
																			●		●

Name

Dotty numbers

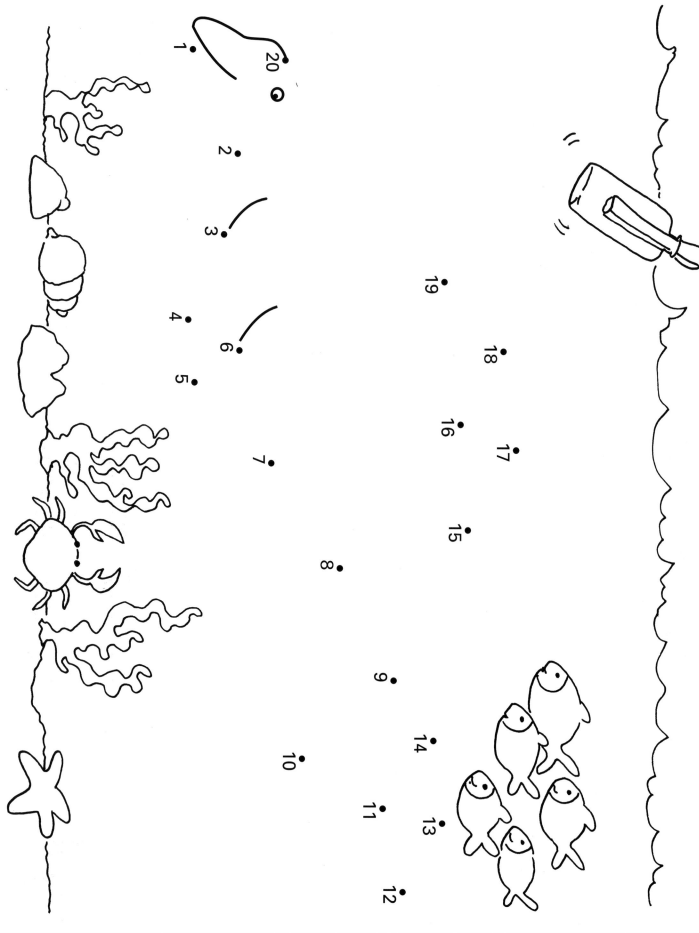

Name

....

Party pieces

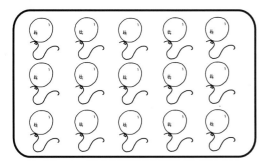

15 fifteen

20 twenty

14 fourteen

11 eleven

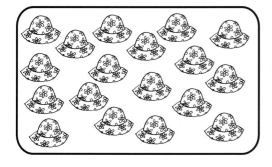

18 eighteen

More party pieces

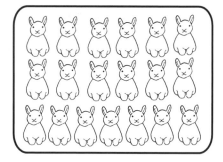 **19** nineteen

 **12** twelve

 **17** seventeen

 **13** thirteen

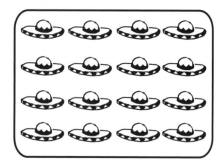 **16** sixteen

Chocolate bars

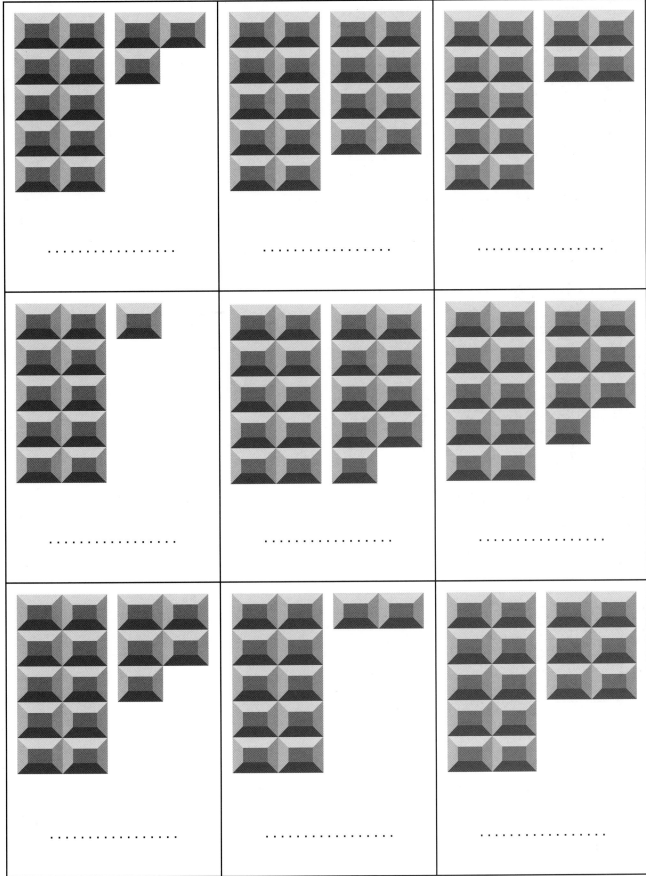

....

....

....

....

....

....

....

....

....

House numbers

1	2
3	4

10 is even

7 is odd

15 is ....

18 is ....

...... is ....

...... is ....

...... is ....

I live on the **odd** side of the street

I live on the **even** side of the street

Name ....

Odds and evens

Evens

0 1 2 3 4 5 6 7 8 9 10 11 12 13 14 15 16 17 18 19 20

Odds

0 1 2 3 4 5 6 7 8 9 10 11 12 13 14 15 16 17 18 19 20

1	2	3	4
5	6	7	8
9	10	11	12
13	14	15	16
17	18	19	20

1	2	3	4	5
6	7	8	9	10
11	12	13	14	15
16	17	18	19	20

Fingers and toes

1	2	3	4
5	6	7	8
9	10	11	12
13	14	15	16
17	18	19	20

1	2	3	4	5
6	7	8	9	10
11	12	13	14	15
16	17	18	19	20

How many?

. . . .

. . . .

. . . .

Number snakes

11
13
15

30
25
20
0

2
4
10 8
16

3
6
9

10
20
30

Multibase numbers

5

1   **2**

Name

....

Abacus numbers

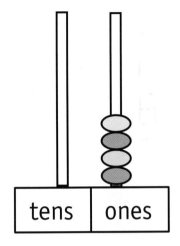

tens	ones

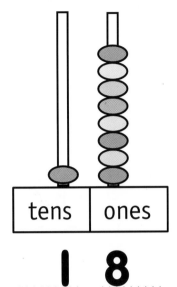

tens	ones

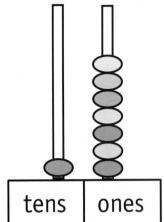

tens	ones

4

1   8

....

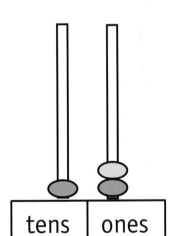

tens	ones

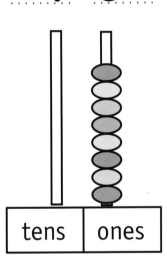

tens	ones

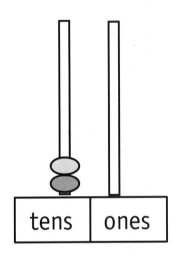

tens	ones

....

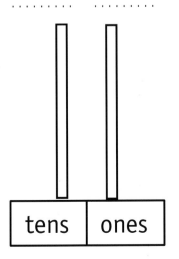

tens	ones

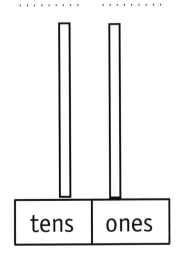

tens	ones

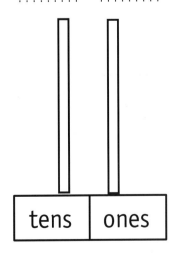

tens	ones

....

Flags

is less than   A number in between is

is less than   A number in between is

is more than   A number in between is

is more than   A number in between is

is . . . . . than   A number in between is

is . . . . . than   A number in between is

is . . . . . than   A number in between is

Name

....

More or less

16   10   **less** .... makes

☐   .... makes   ☐

☐   .... makes   ☐

☐   .... makes   ☐

☐   .... makes   ☐

☐   .... makes   ☐

Name

Ski race

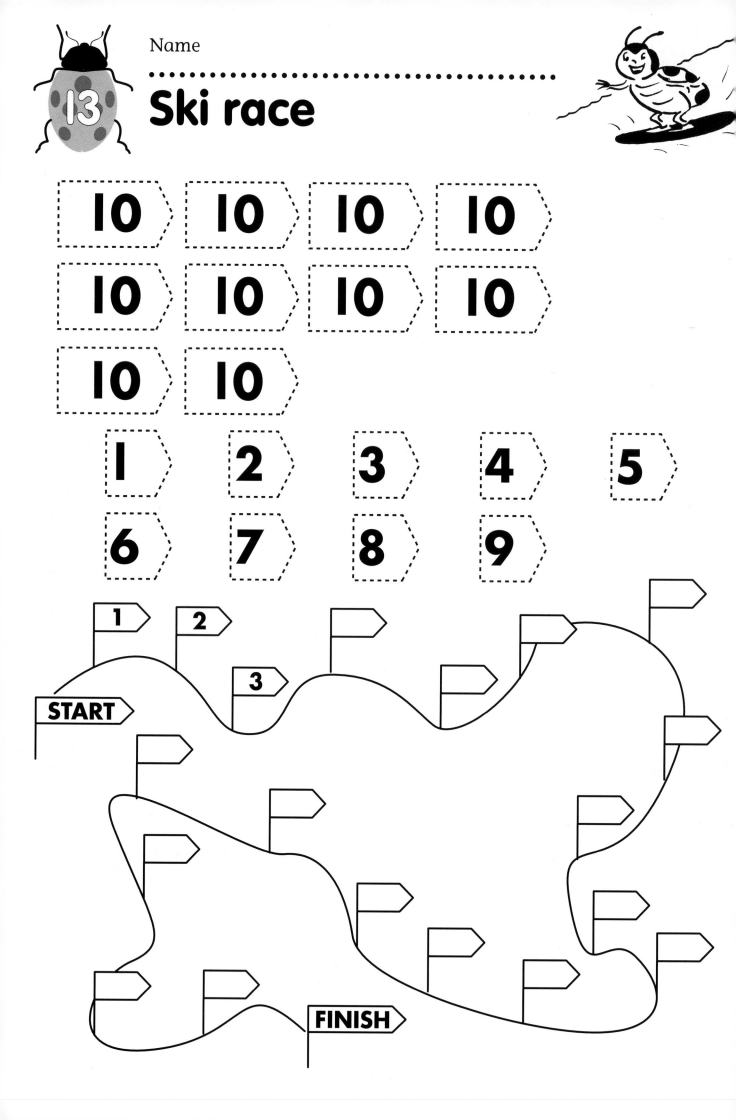

10	10	10	10
10	10	10	10
10	10		

1	2	3	4	5
6	7	8	9	

START

FINISH

14 Number sentences

10	1	9	is	the
10	2	8	and	
10	3	7	more	
10	4	6	less	
10	5	5	than	

makes equals minus

difference between

subtract take away

Domino sums

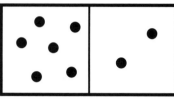

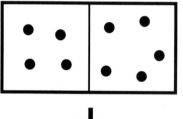 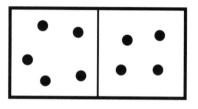

2 + 6 = ...   **6 + 2 = ...**

...... + ... = ...   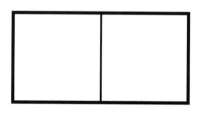

...... + ... = ...

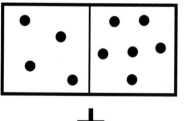

...... + ... = ... + ... = ...

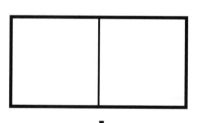

...... + ... = ... + ... = ...

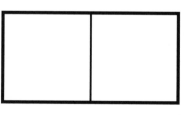

...... + ... = ... + ... = ...

Connect 3

3	2	5	1	6	3
3	1	4	3	2	5
4	5	1	4	2	2
3	2	5	3	2	3
5	1	4	6	6	4
4	3	6	1	2	1

Name

....

The story of _____

.... + ... = ...

.... + ... = ...

.... + ... = ...

.... + ... = ...

.... + ... = ...

.... + ... = ...

.... + ... = ...

.... + ... = ...

.... + ... = ...

.... + ... = ...

Name

What's left?

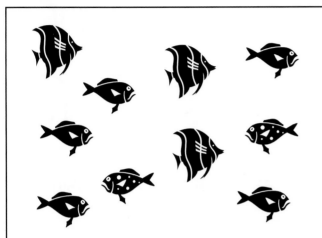

10 fish

Cover up **3**

How many left? . . . .

10 - 3 = ☐

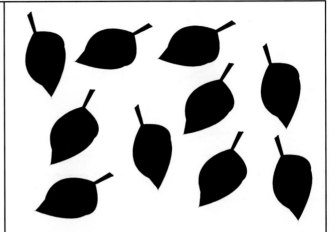

10 leaves

Cover up **5**

How many left? . . . .

10 - 5 = ☐

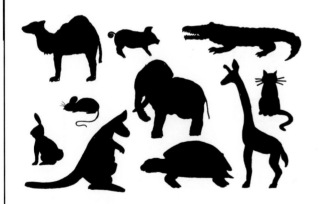

10 animals

Cover up . . . .

How many left? . . . .

10 - . . . . = ☐

10 people

Cover up . . . .

How many left? . . . .

10 - . . . . = ☐

Grouping 5s

 8 is 5 add 3

6 is 5 add 1

14

| 5 | 5 | 3 | 1 |

0 1 2 3 4 5 6 7 8 9 10 11 12 13 14 15 16 17 18 19 20

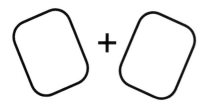 .... is 5 add ....

.... is 5 add ....

0 1 2 3 4 5 6 7 8 9 10 11 12 13 14 15 16 17 18 19 20

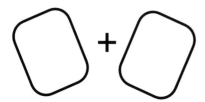 .... is 5 add ....

.... is 5 add ....

0 1 2 3 4 5 6 7 8 9 10 11 12 13 14 15 16 17 18 19 20

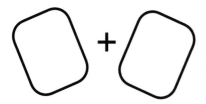 .... is 5 add ....

.... is 5 add ....

0 1 2 3 4 5 6 7 8 9 10 11 12 13 14 15 16 17 18 19 20

20 Next-door numbers

6 ⬚⬚⬚⬚⬚⬚ is the
                same as
+

7 ⬚⬚⬚⬚⬚⬚⬚

6 ⬚⬚⬚⬚⬚⬚
+

6+1 ⬚⬚⬚⬚⬚⬚ ⬚

$$6 + 7 = 6 + 6 + 1$$
$$= 12 + 1$$
$$= 13$$

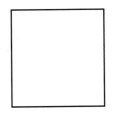 +  =

 +  =

 +  =

 +  =

 +  =

Add 9 machines

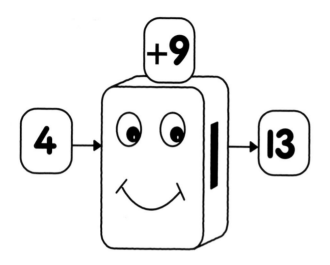

$$4 \quad + \quad 9 = \quad 13$$

.... + 9 = ...

.... + 9 = ...

.... + 9 = ...

.... + 9 = ...

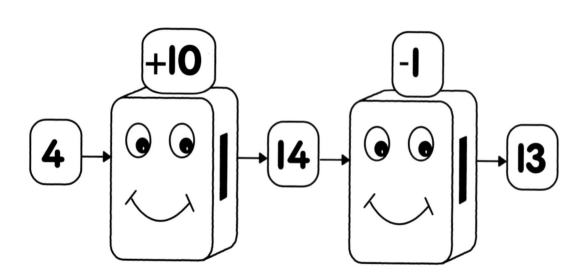

$$4 + 10 = \quad 14$$

.... + 10 = ...

.... + 10 = ...

.... + 10 = ...

.... + 10 = ...

$$14 - 1 = \quad 13$$

.... - 1 = ...

.... - 1 = ...

.... - 1 = ...

.... - 1 = ...

22 Grouping 10s

13 is 10 add 3

11 is 10 add 1

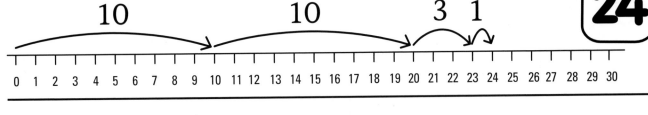

24

10   10   3   1

0 1 2 3 4 5 6 7 8 9 10 11 12 13 14 15 16 17 18 19 20 21 22 23 24 25 26 27 28 29 30

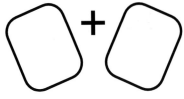

.... is 10 add ....

.... is 10 add ....

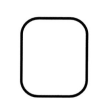

0 1 2 3 4 5 6 7 8 9 10 11 12 13 14 15 16 17 18 19 20 21 22 23 24 25 26 27 28 29 30

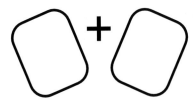

.... is 10 add ....

.... is 10 add ....

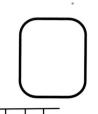

0 1 2 3 4 5 6 7 8 9 10 11 12 13 14 15 16 17 18 19 20 21 22 23 24 25 26 27 28 29 30

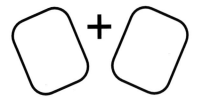

.... is 10 add ....

.... is 10 add ....

0 1 2 3 4 5 6 7 8 9 10 11 12 13 14 15 16 17 18 19 20 21 22 23 24 25 26 27 28 29 30

Name

Needs and leaves

18 + 5

That needs
2

That leaves
3

18   20   23

23

18 + 7

That needs
. . . .

That leaves
. . . .

18   20

That needs
. . . .

That leaves
. . . .

16 + 6

That needs
. . . .

That leaves
. . . .

16   20

That needs
. . . .

That leaves
. . . .

19 + 5

That needs
. . . .

That leaves
. . . .

19 20

That needs
. . . .

That leaves
. . . .

Think of a number

I think of a number.
I add **4** and I get **7**.
What was my
number?

7 take away **4** makes **3**.

3.
The answer is **3**!

I think of a number.
I add **2** and I get **6**.
What was my
number?

The answer is ......

I think of a number.
I take away **3** and I get **5**.
What was my
number?

The answer is ......

I think of a number.
I take away **6** and I get **3**.
What was my
number?

The answer is ......

I think of a number.
I add **7** and I get **12**.
What was my
number?

The answer is ......

25 Tree puzzle

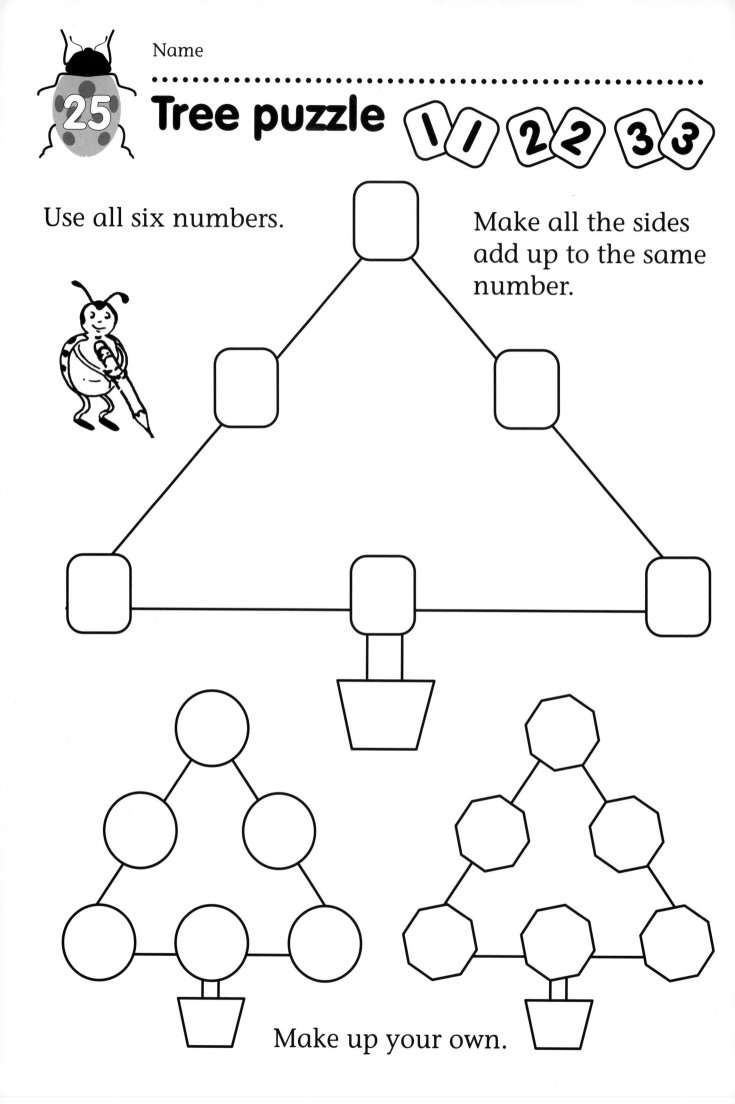

Use all six numbers.

Make all the sides add up to the same number.

Make up your own.

Darts

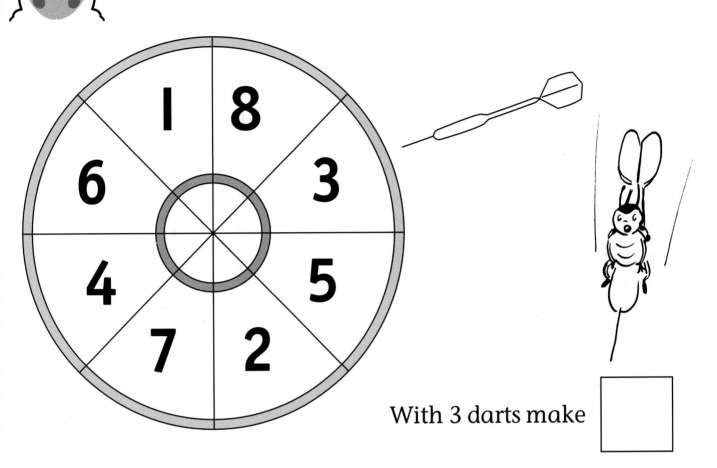

With 3 darts make ▢

Find lots of ways.

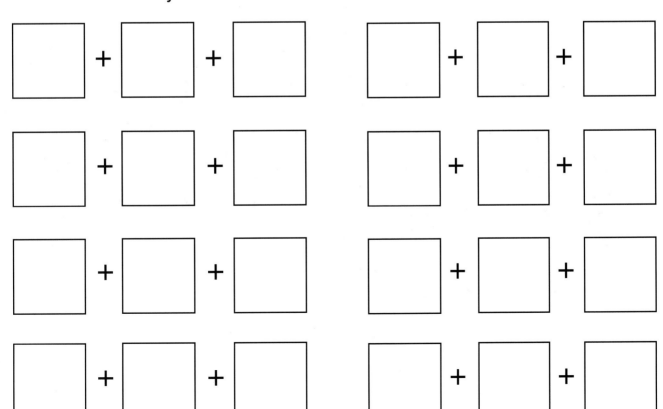

▢ + ▢ + ▢   ▢ + ▢ + ▢

▢ + ▢ + ▢   ▢ + ▢ + ▢

▢ + ▢ + ▢   ▢ + ▢ + ▢

▢ + ▢ + ▢   ▢ + ▢ + ▢

Name

Tell me a story

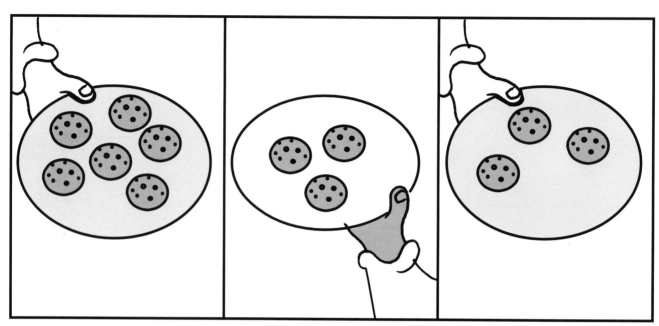

I had six buns. Jasmine came in.
I gave her three buns.
I had three buns left.

$6 - 3 = 3$

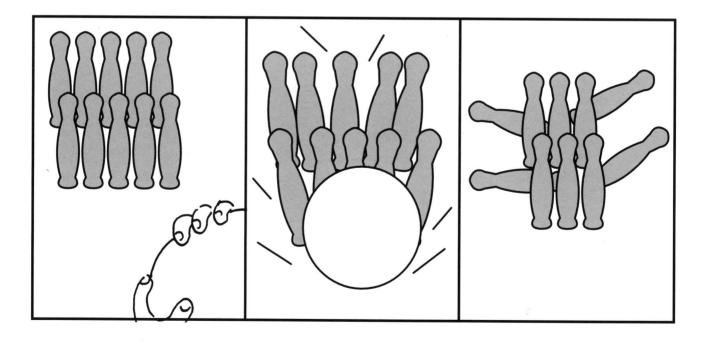

Ways to pay

Name

....

pay 5p

another way

another way

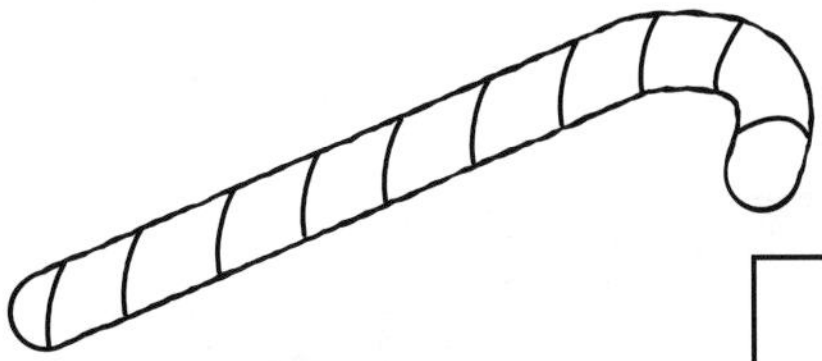

pay 6p

another way

another way

Name

....

Change game

18p

13p

12p

11p

15p

19p

16p

17p

14p

School fair

Coconut shy **14p**		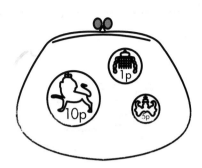
Lucky ducks **16p**		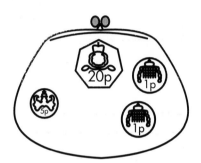
Treasure Hunt **18p**		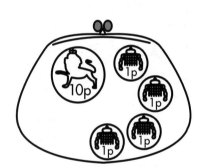
Bran Tub **21p**		
Shove a penny **27p**	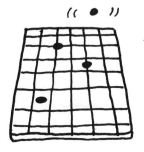	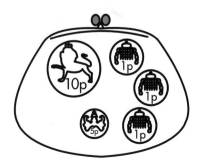